© Dave Broadfoot 2010

Published by The Bluecoat Press, Liverpool
Book design by Michael March, Liverpool
Printed by Grafo (Spain)

ISBN 9781904438977

The Adventures of Billy'r Kid

By Dave Broadfoot

THE BLUECOAT PRESS

..AND SO EVERYONE WAS ROUNDED UP FOR SCHOOL.
NOW, STEVIE Y'READY..
O.K..BYE, MAM....
TAKE A BROLLY YOU'LL CATCH YOUR DEATH..
I HAVE ENOUGH GRIEF IN SCHOOL.. WITHOUT TAKE'N' A BROLLY MAM!
....SO..ER.. BIG JOHN, ..YOU KNOW IT'S TEEM'N' DOWN!..DO'NT YOU??
THAT'S WHY I'VE GOT ME CAP ON STE!
OH YEAH... RIGHT!

...BUT YOU'D GET THE CANE!
C'MON LADS!
SO WE LEFT MRS MAC; DOING WHAT SHE DID BEST..... GUIDING KIDS SAFELY ACROSS THE ROAD... GIVING DRIVERS HEART ATTACKS, AND INTRODUCING KIDS TO STRANGE AND EXOTIC WORDS...WHICH IF REPEATED IN FRONT OF PARENTS OR TEACHERS USUALLY GOT YOU A CRACK!
MORN 'N' MRS MAC!
MORN 'N' MY LAMBS
STOP
SCREEEEECCCHHHH
BEEEEEEP

14

16

YOU GET THE IDEA... BUT THIS WAS FRIDAY, AND FRIDAY HAD THE WORST ORDEAL OF ANY SCHOOL DAY... FOOTBALL.... THAT MIGHT SOUND STRANGE, COMING FROM A SCOUSER, BUT... READ ON.....

.... FIRST, MORNING ASSEMBLY.

WHERE MISS EVANS (THE MUSIC) HAD US SING, LAND OF MY FATHERS; THEN THE HEADMASTER, MR GRIFFITHS GAVE A SERMON ON THE ENGLISH EXPLOITATION OF THE WELSH. FINISHING OFF WITH A ROUSING RENDITION OF MEN OF HARLECH .... AND THEN.

RIGHT YOU HORRIBLE LOT, PICK UP YOUR KIT! 'N' GET DOWNSTAIRS DOUBLE QUICK TIME

THIS COULD CAUSE SOME PROBLEMS, WHICH BECAME APPARENT, ONCE OFF THE BUS...

YOU TWO; WRONG SHORTS!

SHOES ON WRONG FEET, BOY!

SHIRT... BACK TO FRONT

...YOU TWO...

...I GIVE UP! SIGH

MR PRYCE WOULD DIVIDE US INTO TWO TEAMS ... ..THIRTY BOYS (APPROX.) ON EACH TEAM, (WE ONLY HAD THE ONE BALL,). HE THEN SENT THREE BOYS TO EITHER END OF THE PITCH TO ACT AS DEFENDERS AND GOALKEEPER...

FLIPP'N' GREAT... GOALKEEP'N'! ...AGAIN!

AT LEAST IT KEEPS US OUT OF PRYCIES WAY!

'ANG' ON LADS.. ..WAIT FOR ME..

WE'RE LIKE THE THREE MUSKETEERS.. ...ONE FOR ALL ..... AYE

21

NOW YOU MIGHT BE THINKING, 'HANG ON, ISN'T THERE A FOOTY MATCH GOING ON HERE?'...WELL 'YES' AND 'NO'. YOU SEE THIS IS A 1950's GAME OF FOOTBALL, SO IT'S NOTHING LIKE THE GAME OF TODAY. 'WHY NOT'? YOU ASK, WELL, BECAUSE WE DIDN'T HAVE A 'GIRLY' PLASTIC BALL TO KICK AROUND..'OH NO'..WE HAD A LEATHER CASE BALL, WHICH WAS BASICALLY THE SAME WEIGHT AS A CANNONBALL!

...SO THE GAME VERY RARELY MOVED BEYOND A COUPLE OF YARDS (METERS!) FROM THE CENTRE SPOT.

LEAVING THOSE DEFENDING THE GOAL, PLENTY OF TIME TO CONTEMPLATE THEIR NAVELS...

26

THE TALES OF BILLY - KID

THE FISH

LIVERPOOL'S, EVERTON VALLEY ... IN THE MID 1950'S. AN AREA STILL CARRYING THE SCARS OF THE MAY 1940'S BLITZ, THE COUNTRY JUST COMING OFF RATIONING, BUT STILL WITH EVERYTHING IN SHORT SUPPLY .... EXCEPT, KIDS ... THESE ARE THE BABY BOOM YEARS .... AND HUMOUR; SOMETHING LIVERPOOL HAS NEVER BEEN SHORT OF.

51

GOING TO THE OUTSIDE TOILET;. AT NIGHT ALWAYS FILLED ME WITH TREPIDATION... .. (AMONG OTHER THINGS).. IT WAS COLD, (USUALLY).. AND DARK;..WELL, APART FROM THE LIGHTS FROM THE SURROUNDING HOUSES... AND YOUR TORCH OR CANDLE...`MAYBE` A FULL MOON!.. BUT BASICALLY, PITCH BLACK.... AND SCARY!! . THANK GOD I HAD MY BIG SISTER TO LOOK OUT FOR ME!!!!

58

67

 SOMETHING ARE YOUNGER READERS MIGHT NOT KNOW.. ...BACK IN THE 1950'S, CHILDREN TRAVELLED THE LENGTH AND BREADTH OF THE LAND BY HANGING ON TO AN ADULTS (USUALLY FEMALE... .HOPEFULLY YOUR MUMS.)... SKIRT OR COAT.. NOBODY PAID ANY ATTENTION TO A KID... SO LONG AS IT WAS ATTACHED IN THIS MANNER.   HENCE →

HHHMMM?

EXCUSE ME MADAM!

...ILD !!

ABOUT YOUR CHILD!

YOU MUST BE MISTAKEN... I HAVE NO CH..

One of the key points about hiding is to learn stillness.. Because, as most animals know, movement attracts attention!

THE END

ONLY THE PUBS OUTNUMBERED THE CINEMAS..
...YOU COULD FIND A MOVIE THEATRE EVERY
COUPLE OF HUNDRED YARDS (METRES!), BACK IN
THE 50's.... IT'S SATURDAY MORNING, SO IT
MUST BE THE SATURDAY MATINEES!!....
CARTOONS, A CLIFF HANGER SERIAL, PATHE NEWS
(I LOVED THAT CROWING COCKEREL),... A MAIN FEATURE
FILM.... PLUS, COMPETITIONS UP ON THE STAGE...
ALL FOR THE PRICE OF AN ENTRY TICKET...'COURSE'
IF YOU DIDN'T HAVE THE CASH FOR A TICKET... THERE
WAS ALWAYS, THE CUNNING PLAN!!!

THE TALES OF PAM ~ KID

THE DUCK APPLE NIGHT (HALLOWEEN) TALES

BACK THEN HALLOWEEN WAS CELEBRATED BY PLAYING, BOBBING AND DUCKING, FOR APPLES ...

BOBBING :- APPLES HANG FROM A PIECE OF STRING; YOU THEN TRY TO EAT THEM, WHILST BLINDFOLDED; AND WITHOUT USING YOUR HANDS ..... DUCKING :- APPLES FLOATING IN WATER, AGAIN, USING ONLY YOUR MOUTH YOU HAVE TO TRY AND DIP ONE OUT.

I LIKE IT!

IS YOUR KID O.K. CHARLOTTE?

NO CHEATING, WILLIAM!

WITH SOME MATES, WALNUTS AND MUMS ROCK HARD TOFFEE, WE HAD A WHALE OF A TIME.

AT THE END OF THE EVENING, MUM WOULD THROW
A BLANKET OVER THE TABLE, AND US KIDS WOULD
CLIMB UNDERNEATH TO TELL GHOST STORIES.

101

footer:

THEN OVER THE NEXT COUPLE OF WEEKS, THE BOBBIES START TO GET REPORTS OF PEOPLE BEING ATTACKED BY A CAT!... THAT BITES OUT THEIR TONGUE... THESE ARE USUALLY NAGGING WIVES OR MOANING HUSBANDS.

118

THE END